Wonderful Worlds

Edited By Debbie Killingworth

First published in Great Britain in 2019 by:

 YoungWriters® Est. 1991

Young Writers
Remus House
Coltsfoot Drive
Peterborough
PE2 9BF
Telephone: 01733 890066
Website: www.youngwriters.co.uk

FOREWORD

Here at Young Writers, we love to let imaginations run wild and creativity go crazy. Our aim is to encourage young people to get their creative juices flowing and put pen to paper. Each competition is tailored to the relevant age group, hopefully giving each pupil the inspiration and incentive to create their own piece of creative writing, whether it's a poem or a short story. By allowing them to see their own work in print, we know their confidence and love for the written word will grow.

For our latest competition Poetry Wonderland, we invited primary school pupils to create wild and wonderful poems on any topic they liked – the only limits were the limits of their imagination! Using poetry as their magic wand, these young poets have conjured up worlds, creatures and situations that will amaze and astound or scare and startle! Using a variety of poetic forms of their own choosing, they have allowed us to get a glimpse into their vivid imaginations. We hope you enjoy wandering through the wonders of this book as much as we have.

CONTENTS

Independent Entries

Aisha Mao (8)	1
Eve Rae Olea Turner (11)	2
Conrad Van Wyk (9)	5
Olivia Lubczynska (11)	6
Rebekah Zara Murphy (13)	8
Mehreen Shahzad (10)	10
Ava Kelly-Parker (9)	12
Lilly-Rose Edmond (11)	14
Anush Shashikanth (11)	16
Ayaan Ahmed	18
Sanuka Kudaligama (11)	20
Meng Tong Yin (11)	22
Gurkamalpreet Dhaliwal	24
Jack Hei Lee (9)	26
Eunice Opemipo Olagbolabo (9)	28
Andre Henri Josse (8)	30
Avin Welsh (9)	32
Oliver Joseph John Smith (10)	34
Temiloluwa Emmanuel Kalejaiye (9)	36
Gisele Liesl Edwards (9)	38
Ahmed Mohamed Efhil (7)	40
Louis Emile Josse (10)	42
Anne-Marie Mensah (9)	43
Natalia Tyl (9)	44
Rahavy Selvarajah (10)	45
Leah Brown (8)	46
Faatimah Raja (6)	48
Sahar Zarina Hamdard (10)	50
Andrew Simeon Glore (8)	52
Maryam Gurjee (11)	53
Abigail Keen (9)	54
Daniel F T Joaille-Burge (8)	55
Caitlin Tierney (9)	56
Zainab Raja (8)	58
Haniyah Iman Yaqub (9)	60
Phoebe Sims	61
Kylah Wishart (10)	62
Elana Natalya Cuthbert (11)	63
Nana Adu Boateng	64
Alfie John Parsons (7)	65
Ini Rowaiye	66
William He (11)	67
Logan Carter (10)	68
Harry Egbayelo (10)	70
Joel Choe Davies (12)	71
Ethan Darren Walker (9)	72
Chejen Satchithananthan	73
Haseena Sophia Hamdard	74
Zacharia Shafique (8)	75
Sabaa Jauhar (11)	76
Ivani Patel (8)	77
Joe Roy (11)	78
Ovin Indiv Wasala Mudiyanselage (6)	79
Oscar Mackenzie Terrell (9)	80
Delisha Meghal Vora (7)	81
James Andradi	82
Inaya Mohamed	83
Hope Whittaker (5)	84
Rhys Thornton	85
Eva Maria Sirusaite (9)	86
Arabella Bage (6)	87
Hafsa Sultan (7)	88
Akshay Nar (7)	89
Ayomide Deborah Aboyeji (10)	90
Kai Runaghan (8)	91

Foxdale Primary School, Higher Foxdale

Ezrianne Shaw (7)	92
Zoe Elizabeth Neuwirt (8)	94
Elizabeth Campbell (9)	95
Pippa Harrison (7)	96
Lyra Kate Skillen (8)	97
Liberty Delooze (8)	98
Emily McCarrick (8)	99
Amira Howard Murtagh (9)	100
Ethan Thomas Hannay (7)	101
Connor Maginn (8)	102
Poppy Taylor-Smith (7)	103
Spencer Brown (8)	104
Keira Cubbon (7)	105

St Johns CE Middle School, Bromsgrove

Molly Joanne Anderson (10)	106
Katie Lloyd (9)	108
Leah Thompson (10)	110
Fjola O'Donnell (10)	112
Ella Hinson (10)	114
Felicity Crowther (9)	115
Charlotte Collier (10)	116
Floyd Coppack Stevens (10)	117
Ellie Booth (10)	118
Ollie Squire (10)	119
Pheobie Taylor (9)	120
Alivia Harriet Faulkner (9)	121
Drew Dalton (9)	122
Erin Elizabeth Hughes (10)	123
Freya Snead (10)	124
Sam Dufficey (9)	125
Jack Wykes (9)	126
Isla Masson (9)	127
Harrison Biddlestone (10)	128
Edward Melarkey (10)	129
Tom Webber (9)	130
William Millership (10)	131
Flynn Cleaver (9)	132
Jake Shiels (10)	133

Elizabeth Green (10)	134
Isabelle Johnson (10)	135
Frederick George Spencer Parsons (9)	136
Josh De Waal (9)	137
Ayvah Lawther (9)	138
Arthur Ingram (9)	139
Max English (9)	140
Sam Wheatcroft (10)	141
Grace Rutherford (9)	142
Heidi Dews (9)	143
Corey Bacciochi (9)	144
Harry Astin (10)	145

THE POEMS

Aisha In Wonderland

I seek adventures,
I want to go to a place where there are weird
creatures,
Like a green cat asking for friendship,
Or a funny jelly tree that likes to eat chips.

I'm taking one nervous step into a swirling hole,
My brain telling me to stop,
But my heart wanting to explore,
In the end, my curiosity pulls me into Wonderland.

I think my eyes are tricking me and I'm going crazy,
I see wild and wonderful creatures,
And I wonder who rules this Wonderland,
A prince, a princess, a queen, a king or maybe me.

Another swirling hole,
It's time to go, or there's time to stay,
Another wonder and adventure awaits me,
Maybe there will be witches and wizards,
Magic and wonders that no one knows.

Aisha Mao (8)

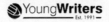

Unicorns On The Moon

In the night sky
The stars were smiling bright and giddy
There a small, joyful girl was staring and
Her name was Lily
She always wondered about space
And what could be in that wonderful place

Morning arose
She walked down on her tippy toes
She got out her cereal and her spoon
Wondering if unicorns were on the moon

Lily noticed a door
Her smile, her grin, Lily was
Curious and stepped right in...

A whole new world was revealed
But she couldn't go back, the door was sealed
She entered some sort of wonderland!
She would never forget it, for it was so grand

Pink coloured the skies
It was beauty to her eyes

Flowers danced
While horses pranced
Pink, purple, blue and green
Were all the colours to be seen
Extraordinary elephants, daring dragons
This was her true dream where the magic happens
Birds past and sang a peaceful tune
Lily was still wondering if unicorns were on the
moon

Could they live there?
Do they even exist?
Do you know?
Can they fly across the mist?
The stars in this world were different, they smiled
They waved,
They even played

Then a fairy came by
She fluttered her wings and by Lily she flew
"Your wishes, your dreams, your deepest desires
Come to me to reinvent wires,"
The fairy exclaimed!

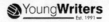

She was in delight to hear what the girl would say
"Take me to the moon with a unicorn I can play!"
Zip, zap, zong!
Magic and wonders whispered along
After swirling her wand, *poof!*
She appeared to the moon, it didn't take long
The most mindboggling sight was she before her eyes...
A unicorn was there to her surprise!

They flew into the breeze
The sunset and stars
It was truly the best day of her life
For they even rode to Mars
Day by day once she had left the wonderland
Lily would say, "Me and my unicorn
Together we'll be
Just stay by my side
And we will soar across the seas."

Eve Rae Olea Turner (11)

Around The World

I have a game I love to play,
Where I close my eyes and fly away.
From London to Paris, New York to Hong Kong,
I go on adventures, dream on, dream on.

On the White Cliffs of Dover, I could see Paris,
I would like to go there but my French does
embarrass

In New York City stood a neon-lit tree,
Where skyscrapers rise over the land of the free.

Hong Kong is a city of impressive technology,
And since '97 no longer a colony.

On Venice's canals while rowing and thinking,
I had an odd feeling... *The city is sinking!*

So fly away at the speed of light,
Ten million times around the world tonight.
From London to Paris, New York to Hong Kong.
The world is your oyster, dream on, dream on.

Conrad Van Wyk (9)

The Voice Of The Moon

The moon whispers in my ear, as I lie on the grass,
gazing into the empty void above me.
Stars fall into place,
like the first couple of paint splodges that lie on an
empty canvas.
The first couple of steps towards the artist's
creation.
The moon shines onto the world beneath it; our
world,
ruined with deforestation, littering, and war.
The ozone layer, crumbling away, like a crust.
The moon listens to the beautiful animals
populating our world,
many singing their last song
or roaring for the last time.
It listens to trees fall to the ground,
plastic hitting the earth
and gunshots, echoing in the ears of innocent
children.
It looks down on the world
and sees the heated arguments between political
leaders.

It sees the racism, sexism
and the barrier between acceptance and gender
equality.
It sees the world, riddled with destruction,
it's up to us to change this,
to take care of the world,
and accept each other for who we are.
It's up to us to stop bullying and help people in
dismay.
The voice of the moon whispers in my ear,
as I lie on the grass, gazing into the empty void
above me.
"One day, it'll happen.
Maybe when you're gone,
maybe when you're alive.
But one day, it will happen..."

Olivia Lubczynska (11)

A Walk In 'Wonderland'

A walk in Wonderland, what do you see?
Do you see flowers, little buzzing bees?
Do you see towers and castles galore?
Do you see the future and what lies in store?

A walk in Wonderland, what could be?
Could I be a princess going for afternoon tea?
Could I be a hero saving cats from an oak tree?
What would be the right path for me?

In Wonderland, I could be anything!
I don't have to be what's been written before
I could be the new book in the store!
I don't have to be a pretty princess
Instead, for instance, I could be...

Me on my birthday in ten years
walking down the street waving
to all my peers!
Me in a dress, heading for a dance
but then take a chance
and fall into a deep romance!

I could be just like me! No glitz, no glam
A plain old story, just dark, no fame
But that could be the best of all!
Reality blooming! No fiction or faux!
Just what's happening right now
Easy come, easy go!

Wonderland sounds like a dream
come true!
But brains piling up with stuff
that's so not true!
So when I get my shot in this big,
big world...
I'll write down my feelings, let it all loose
because one day, that's how I'll introduce!

Rebekah Zara Murphy (13)

Sweetropolis

In my dream land, all of your wishes will come true.

There are the marshmallow boats
With lollipop oars,
Drifting on the wavy hot chocolate river.
The piped buttercream grass,
With sugar flowers beginning to bloom.
The myriad of treats just waiting to be discovered;
In Sweetropolis, you'll always find something right
for you.

There are the illusionary bites -
A sweet that tastes like whatever you want it to.
Or the infinite gobstoppers -
Once it dissolves, it instantly grows back
You'll never need to waste your pocket money
again!

There are candy cane trees,
Inhabited by milk chocolate monkeys,
Or the chocolate bunnies hopping around joyfully
And you can't forget the candyfloss unicorns,

Whinnying and tossing their heads around gently
Or galloping about as swift as the wind.

Amazing things happen in Sweetropolis,
In my dream land.

Mehreen Shahzad (10)

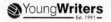

My Favourite Moments In Year 4

I've had lots of fun in Year 4,
I wish I could spend time in here even more,
But my favourite memory out of all,
Has to be Condover Hall,
The leap of faith and the climbing wall,
The abseiling and the sensory trail,
And from the mums and dads, all the mail.

Here comes the second best,
This choice is tastier than the rest,
The chocolate workshop,
The chocolate spilt all down my top,
One of my favourites, the tasty treat,
It was so nice to meet,
The delicious chocolate, 'twas so nice and sweet.

My third favourite choice has to be,
The recycled instruments made by me,
We used up all the sticky tape,

And twanged our elastic bands until our
instruments took shape,
Right at the end,
When they were all taped up and would no longer
bend,
We formed a unique class band,
The plucking and the drumming together sounded
grand.

Those were my favourites, but I have to go,
Go to Year 5 and grow.

Ava Kelly-Parker (9)

Silence

Silence, silence all around.
Silence in the air, silence on the ground.
The only noise to be heard
Was the sun opening its blinds
To wake the forest and the leaves on the ground.

As the honey-yellow sun shone through
A kingdom arose just like me and you.
The bears started to hunt for the kings
As the youngest awoke to see what they may bring

The kingdom was bustling and working
And watching flowers grow.
And as time took its toll it was now lunch
And the king of the bucks came to patrol

Now these bucks were rulers
And kept an eye on the land
From the heights of mystic treetops
And over cloudy sands;
The bucks had finally seen it all.
Finally the youngest came and called,
"It's bedtime now for all."

So, at last there was...
Silence, silence once more,
Silence all around, silence in the air,
And silence on the ground.

Lilly-Rose Edmond (11)

Snow

Snow is pure and white,
When you look at it your mind turns bright.

It floats angelically in the sky,
And comes floating down like a butterfly.

It is soothing and crunchy under your feet,
It is like walking on one immense sheet.

Snow is as amazing and as fun as can be,
You feel like snuggling in it with your bedtime tea.

When you glance at it an idea flourishes in your
mind,
An idea you want to to keep and don't want to
hide.

Your idea is colossal and you can do what you can,
An idea where you build your own snowman.

This snowman will have a scarf, gloves, stick hands
and a carrot for a nose,
Just one more thing, it has to strike a pose.

This snowman is beautiful and has no worries or strife,
Let's hope, just one day it will come to life.

Anush Shashikanth (11)

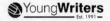

Harry Potter Land

I see Harry Potter here
If Voldemort appears I'll be in fear

Up goes the Ford Anglia with a horn
Who is driving, maybe the Weasley twins or Ron?

There goes Hermione Granger
She uses magic when we are in danger

Draco the rude one
He bullies me for fun

Albus Dumbledore is the head
Snape made him dead

I see Sirius Black
He has to hide before he gets hacked

Dudley Dursley is Harry's cousin who is rude
His friends call him a dude

I get my snacks at Three Broomsticks
Maybe you get zoom sticks

Minerva McGonagall, the head of my house
She transfigures into a cat, not a mouse

I see Quidditch players on the field
No, no, they use a broom not a wheel

Hagrid is my favourite adult
It was the first day's result

Bye-bye Wizard Land
I hope for remembrance I get a wrist band

I still taste the butterbeer 'n' cream
I wonder if all this was just a dream?

Ayaan Ahmed

The Selfish Monkey

In a swampy jungle, far, far away
In the trees, down in the bay,

An orange monkey jumps around,
He turns up the music to make more sound,
Boom, boom the ground shakes,
The louder the music, the more noise he'll make,

He dives into the water to get himself wet,
He's the weirdest monkey you've ever met...!
As the wind blows, the river flows,
Little monkey is making dough,

As the dough goes into the oven tree,
Here comes Mr Bumblebee,
"Can I have some dough? It looks so yummy!
I'm very hungry so it would fill my tummy!"
"No, no, no, Mr Bumblebee,
I've only made dough because it's just for me."

Down flies Mr Bumblebee, looking quite sad,
Then in a second, little monkey feels bad.

"Sorry, Mr Bumblebee for being so rude,
You can come back later when I've cooked more
food."

Sanuka Kudaligama (11)

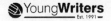

Happy Teacher's Day

Have you noticed children buying presents?
They are buying for their teachers.
Presents are in different sizes.
And presents are in different colours.

Teachers will open the presents with surprised faces.
"Happy Teacher's Day!"
Greetings will be followed by students.
Teachers will burst into tears.
Whole school will be filled with hugs and kisses.

Ceremony will be held and run for a day.
Happy everyone will be.
Easy the day will go.

Red flowers teachers will have in right hands.
On the left will be scrumptious chocolates.
Greeting words will be on the dark red cards.
Happy feelings will be on teachers' faces.

Yes!
At last,
Teachers will announce,
"No homework for you all one day."
Yay! Yay! Yay!

What a great day it will be.
Not only for teachers and students
But also for the nation
That is deeply loved by you and me.

Meng Tong Yin (11)

I Thought I Found A Friend

I thought I found a friend,
Who was always by my side.
I thought I found a friend,
Who always supported me when I cried.
I thought I found a friend,
Who always made me happy.
I thought I found a friend,
Who wasn't bossy or snappy.
We had a blast together; so much fun,
Until one day the time had come.
She said goodbye and moved abroad,
But everyone knows we were like two peas in a
pod.
I cried and cried and cried until I had to move on,
But all I could think about was that she's gone.
Trying to forget all the memories of the past,
I really needed to forget them fast.
As the time passed by quickly,
I found some amazing new friends.
They were just like her
And we made memories that would never end.

But one thing that will never change
Is that she will always be in my heart!

Gurkamalpreet Dhaliwal

Cluckingham Palace

Once there was King Chick,
One day he was sick,
No longer could he click,
Nor kick.

He was married to Queen Cluck,
All the chickens thought she did suck.
She always ate duck
Because it was thought to be good luck.

Cluck only liked fashion,
It was her all-time passion.
When the eagles raided
And took most of the clothes,
The chickens had to ration.
Her face looked ashen
As she had failed the country.

Cluck however only liked food,
He wasn't in a fashion mood,
All who saw him eating food would think he was
very rude
And that is how he made everyone's volume
subdued.

They had a chick, Prince,
Who liked eating mince, ages since.
He said yes to mince but got mixed up with mints.

Eventually, Click died
And Cluck sighed,
This was known worldwide.
When Cluck followed Click's death
They were side by side.

Jack Hei Lee (9)

Riding On A Rainbow

The magical feeling of riding on colours
Making rainbow candyfloss
Sliding down different colours of red,
Orange, yellow, green, blue, indigo, violet!
What joy that comes to my heart at the
Sight of riding on a rainbow!
I arise from the colour red,
The bright sun streaming down
From the first colour to the last.
Shining stars twinkling in the sun
Creating light around the rainbow,
How fun it is to be riding on a rainbow.
When the sun begins to fade,
The colours slowly start to ombre into each other!
It was a beautiful sight and I loved every bit of it!
I was fortunate to be riding on a rainbow
If you ever get a chance to ride on a rainbow,
please go.
Think of all the fantastic things you can eat, play,
explore,
Rainbow everything.

It will surely be a lifetime adventure.
So let's go riding on a rainbow!

Eunice Opemipo Olagbolabo (9)

Connect Land

In Connect Land...
Everything is different than normal...

When you visit the optician,
Or clothes shop or barber,
You look into a candle,
Because it's a mirror!

When Daddy shaves his beard,
The wire might catch fire!

In Connect Land nobody has a car.
You're driven by a mime artist on a boat,
To your destination on the moat.

He'll make you laugh
With his mime of pigs in the bath!

In Connect Land all the flowers move like cats.
They do the floss on purple mats.

About a million miles away
There is a place called Switch Town,

Where the soil is yellow,
And the sun is brown.

I doodle on paintings,
Plain paper is on the wall,
A frog is very big,
And a hippo's very small.

I lived in this place,
But now I must go home.
I will miss you all
But I'll ring you on the phone.

Andre Henri Josse (8)

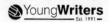

Mysterious Minecraft

I was playing Minecraft
With the console in my hand
Vibrating like a drill
Every time I destroyed a block
I thought that I could hear
Something lurking here and there
Right behind my ear
So then I turned around
Then my TV made a sound
My Minecraft figure had
Come to life on the ground!
I stood there in horror
Not moving a muscle
When my Minecraft figure said,
"Do you want to make a house?"
So I answered like a mouse,
"Yes, sure of course I would."
So with him I placed down some wood
Until I thought I could see
A whole village!
I stood there in glee

For my friend and me
Had made a whole city!
And we both lived together in a mansion
Happily ever after.

Avin Welsh (9)

The Sound Collector

(Based on 'The Sound Collector' by Roger McGough)

A stranger called this morning
Dressed all in black and grey
Put every sound into a bag
And carried them away

The humming of the heater
The ticking of the clock
The stomping of the children
The turning of the lock

The scraping of the windows
The humming of the train
The pitter-patter sound it makes
When you hear the rain

The clanging of the rope
The groaning of the door
The tearing of the paper
The creaking of the floor

The ringing of the bell
The bouncing of the ball
The thudding of the feet
In the great big hall

The tapping of the keyboard
The whistling of the kettle
The humming of the caretaker
Who is called Mr Fettle

A stranger called this morning
He didn't leave his name
Left us only silence
Life will never be the same.

Oliver Joseph John Smith (10)

Unknown World

In the beginning,
The bright green trees,
Added with crunchy apples,
Lots of spring leaves,
Fresh cut grass,
With all the plants,

Sunny days,
Some warm rays,
Burning down,
I don't know how,
The grass is browner than a brownie

In the middle,
Big red nose,
Along with a small scarf,
A rosy glow in my eyes,
Then a big black night,
A Halloween fright,
The bright, huge moon like a silky balloon,
Stars up high in the sky,
People know that it is time.

Snow falls in,
Wind blows out,
Snow splashes,
Wet feet crashes,
Dripping leaves come down,

Big fat coat,
Some skipping boots,
A fluffy hat,
And hairy gloves,

In the end,
Chrismas tree,
Big surprises below,
A huge treat for me,
They are on a show,
This unknown world will bring beautiful things.

Temiloluwa Emmanuel Kalejaiye (9)

Tea Party In Wonderland

I was under my duvet fast asleep,
Lying down on my bed,
The comfy covers on my body
And the pillow resting beneath my head.

So soon, I was in a hot sandy desert
With scorching sand beneath my toes,
I was wondering what had happened;
I was dreaming I suppose!

There were all my toys sitting at the table,
With the wonderful food all out,
It was beautiful, no sound was made,
No one even bothered to shout!

The sandwiches tasted divine
The cakes were great,
And the snacks were amazing
There was nothing I could hate!

I clicked my fingers and I was back in bed,
Fast asleep ready for the morning.

Not a sound I made
Apart from me loudly snoring!

When I woke up
It was the next day,
But sand was in my bed
Was it really a dream or a play?

Gisele Liesl Edwards (9)

Dragon Go Fly, Chicken Go Boom!

Dragon big, dragon scary
Dragon strong, dragon hairy
Up in the sky
The dragon flies
And down below
The people cry
"Dragons are real,
They do fly
With massive wings
They wave goodbye."

With fire from his bottom
And lava out his mouth
This dragon isn't stopping
Cos he's heading down south.
There, lives a chicken
A chicken so brave
It just so happens that
She calls her uncle, Dave
"Have you got some of that magical dust?

The only magical thing I trust
Cos flying for me is a must!"
Today or never

With the dust the
Chicken flies high
Soaring up past the sky
Up above Earth's atmosphere
The dragon now is
Nothing to fear
Dragon small, dragon not scary
Dragon weak, but dragon still hairy.

Ahmed Mohamed Efhil (7)

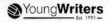

What If?

What if King Kong was only a foot tall,
But in a massive enclosure guarded by 10cm tall
cowboys?

What if the cowboys had squirt guns,
And on their cowboy hats they wore Christmas
trees, even in the summer?
No one was allowed near him because he was too
dangerous.
At least that's what they think!

What if he was actually a baby gorilla
Guarded by cowboys from Zargoland?

What if they heard someone in Zargoland
Talking about him and believed it,
And that's why they captured him?

What if candles were lit by water?
What if dogs were fish in disguise?
What if the world was actually square?
What if phones didn't like people touching them?

Imagine that!

Louis Emile Josse (10)

The Magic Potion

A little bit of this and a little bit of that
All the ingredients landed with a *splat!*
In went the toad legs
Followed by some freshly laid chick eggs
The potion was now starting to stink
It was tempting not to pour it in the sink
Something had to get rid of the smell
It was sure to make someone unwell
But it was too useful so it could not be poured
away
As a matter of fact, the potion would definitely
stay
Some flowers were added to improve the scent
Indeed, the terrible odour had went
All of a sudden the potion lay still
It was ready to go in some magic pots to fill
Once filled, the pots went on a shelf on the wall
Ready to be exhibited in the magic hall.

Anne-Marie Mensah (9)

Protect The World!

Protect! Protect our wonderful animals.
Protect! Protect rainforests from being cut down.
Protect! Protect plant species.
You just *must* understand how important it is,
People just want money,
They don't care about wildlife!
Rainforests give us oxygen,
Don't take the trees!
Bees give honey,
Don't kill bees!
Plants look beautiful in the world,
Don't cut them down!
(Even if they don't do anything,
They at least look nice.)
Stop with pollution, stop with
Cutting rainforests, stop with wrecking
Habitats, stop, stop, *stop!*
This is the world we live in,
So you must understand,
Don't destroy it,
To leave only silence and land.

Natalia Tyl (9)

My Magic Garden

One day I went to my garden and saw
The witches all standing in awe.
I saw Matilda holding a book,
And Miss Trunchbull giving me an icy look.
Out of the corner popped out Charlie
And Willy Wonka with his young son, Marley.

Suddenly out came Jacqueline Wilson
Be careful and try hard to listen.
I saw her taking out my favourite book
She gave it to me with a friendly look.

Then Michael Rosen came into my garden
Don't ask me how because I don't know
We started having a little row,
About who was the best out of us all.

Now this poem comes to an end
I will see you next time my dear friend.

Rahavy Selvarajah (10)

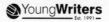

Water Wonderland

A world of mine, a world of wonder
This is how I discovered
Something deep down under
It was a summer's day
Children were at play
And down suntanning I lay
I came up slim
Swore I would swim
Got into the water and swam down low
I saw something above a wave
It may seem surprising...
It was a cave!

I swam deeper and deeper
A bunch of fat fish
In a hive!
I saw them all
Bunched in a ball
Making honey till the rooster called
I saw the ingredients
All local food
But some fish weren't in the mood

It was weird, but it was nice
But I would rather have hot, soggy rice
I swam back up
Catfish following
I tried to lie on the sand
Without swallowing.

Leah Brown (8)

Nonsense Poem

Children struggling in the rain,
Feeling some pain.
If you're coming to stay,
You will have to pay.

"Can I make a cake
Or will you have something we can bake?
Can I give you some water?"
Asked my dear daughter.

Here's little Jack,
Going down the street.
Where do you think he was going?
He needed something to eat!

Ringing a rusty bell,
We're going to sell.
Are you going to yell?
We will give you a shell.

Summer is fun,
I see the bright, bright sun.

When I have some,
Can you come?

The sun is bright,
But you can't have a water fight.
There are lots of lights,
Use your sight!

Faatimah Raja (6)

Glitter Rain In Wonderland

I went outside to see,
The Mad Hatter smiling with glee.
The glitter poured down in Wonderland,
And I saw the grand band.

I ran to the Mad Hatter,
The glitter rain didn't matter.
The Queen of Hearts,
Loved eating glitter tarts.

I went back to the village,
Most people there were British.
The house was very glittery,
The ground was very slippery.

I loved the rain,
Because it was insane.
The rain was bright yellow,
I saw someone eating a glittery marshmallow.

The ground shimmered brightly
And it started to rain more lightly.
My foot made a crunching sound as I stepped,
And I had a little rest and slept.

Sahar Zarina Hamdard (10)

Silly Sauropods

S *wish! Creak! Shatter!*
I n the smelly slide,
L istening in its den,
L umping a nest,
Y elling inside the deadly den is a baby T-rex.

S mashing with a *boom!*
A re the strong sauropods.
U nbelievable!
R unning and attacking a compsognathus,
O utside the dangerous Petrified Forest.
P laying in the desert is a baby stegosaurus,
O n the plains is a pack of allosaurus,
D igging a nest,
S *mash! Thwack! Roar!*

Andrew Simeon Glore (8)

Wonderland

Wonderland, a place to be,
For freedom till the eye can see,
Oh, how lovely it would be,
To have Wonderland, be my destiny.

I love the sky so perfectly high,
And the candyfloss clouds as big as a lie,
With the sweet milkshake rain, I lick whilst I fly,
I wish I never have to say my goodbye.

A place where inspiration comes to you,
Trust me I've been, it is awesome too,
I love the sky, pink not blue,
And everything there is all true.

Leaving was a tragedy,
But soon I will return just wait and see,
I am Maryam and Wonderland is my destiny,
And I live beyond the infinite sea.

Maryam Gurjee (11)

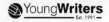

Spooky Wooky

Ooohh, it's icy cold in here
An eerie sinister feeling filled the atmosphere
My hair on my slender back was raised
Like pine needles on trees in a garden maze

The hard boards cracked under every step
I wanted to scream, utter a cry for help
Quivering with fear
I stood frozen right there

I could smell the stench
Water dripping, continuously like an open trench
Closer, louder
I thought my world was over

Suddenly I got the courage
To turn around... be brave
To my amazement... and amusement
I saw a dead rat under a rusty leaking tap
Arising from a tattered old pipe!

Abigail Keen (9)

Daniel And The Bear

Daniel met a big bad bear,
But Daniel didn't really care.
It roared and growled
And was very, very loud.
The bear said, "Daniel, nice to meet you,
Now I will surely eat you."
Daniel groaned and Daniel said,
"If you eat me I'll be dead!"
The bear thought night and day
But still tried to get his way
Then one sunny day Daniel came back.
He came with a rather big rack.
He said to the bear, "You are pretty rare
But you look cold so lie on this rack."
Then Daniel left him on his own
And the bear got sunburn on his back.

Daniel F T Joaille-Burge (8)

Unicorns Flossing On Rainbows

Unicorn, unicorn
with a rainbow horn
Unicorn, unicorn
is a bit bored

Flossing on rainbows is the best
thing she does
But she's quite fussy
What shall she do?

Unicorn, unicorn
Flossing on rainbows
Unicorns, unicorns
Standing on her tiptoes

Dancing and prancing
Is the best thing
But flossing is so
Much better than
Dancing with you!

Unicorn, unicorn
With a rainbow horn
Unicorn, unicorn is
A bit bored.

Caitlin Tierney (9)

Books

Books are nice,
Books are fun.
Books are good for everyone.

I love books,
They are interesting.
I'm sure you'll like them,
As much as I do.

They'll make you intelligent,
They'll make you clever.
They'll make you educated,
As better than ever.

Books are full of secrets,
Which nobody knows.
You'll have to start reading them,
As you grow.

Do you like books?
I hope you do.
They are full of excitement
And full of facts.

You can learn a lot of things,
From only one book.
So why don't you start reading,
Until you get the hook!

Zainab Raja (8)

My Poem About Water

Water, water, everywhere you are
Water, water, isn't really far!
We get it through our house
Underneath your little mouse
Water, water, everywhere
We use it to clean our underwear

Water is a solid, liquid or a gas
Its chemical formula is H2O!
This is awesomely cool, whoa!
Water, water everywhere!
Put your water butt out like you just don't care

Water, water, everywhere
We use it like we just don't care!
We need to be careful because one day 'it' may
not care!
We need to respect and not disrespect!
Water, water, we need to care.

Haniyah Iman Yaqub (9)

The Story Of Pink Unicorns!

Pink, fluffy unicorns, dancing on rainbows,
They thought they were the best.

The walnut,
Devoured by pink, fluffy unicorns,
Never to be seen again.

The walnut returned,
Pink, fluffy unicorns were surprised,
Everyone was spooked.

A pumpkin came,
He killed everyone there,
Never to be seen again.

Then the vampire came and sucked my blood,
Vanished into thin air.

News was broadcasting live, they died,
Only the vampire survived. Oh gawd!

Phoebe Sims

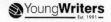

I Invited A Huge Cat To Tea

I heard a strange bang on the door,
But to my surprise I saw,
A huge cat turning round and round,
And he was making an odd cat sound.

I opened the door very wide,
Then the cat came inside,
I gave him a big bowl of tea,
Then he jumped with glee.

I didn't have his favourite food,
So he got in a terrible mood,
He couldn't believe,
When I asked him to leave.

He jumped on his chair,
And growled like an angry bear,
"That's not fair!"
And with that I said, "I don't care, get out there!"

Kylah Wishart (10)

The Stunning Sakura

The stunning sakura peering about,
First left, then right, ever so stout,
Blossoming, blooming in an essence of life,
The aura of invincibility drives away lurking strife.

The flowers swaying in the gentle breeze,
Could bring a person to their knees,
Majestic it stands isolated,
Where long ago a bluebird mated,

The blossom falls,
The blue moon rises above the lifeless world,
Its grace and glory seeps away,
Inviting spirits to come and play.

The pink flower's dance is so picturesque,
It's etched in my mind.

Elana Natalya Cuthbert (11)

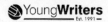

The Crazy Alien

Once upon a time,
There lived a crazy alien!
He once saw a white 'Looby' and the Looby it was
very lazy.
"What is your name?" the alien asked
But *frightened* was the little Looby!
It turned into a mouse,
The alien - a shark!
The shark *ate* the mouse...
But it turned into a Looby again!
"Urgh!" said the shark and an alien it became,
Spat out the Looby,
And the Looby ran away.

Nana Adu Boateng

The Magic Box

(Based on 'Magic Box' by Kit Wright)

I will put in the box...
A boat to sail to faraway lands,
My brother's voice that is loud,
A piece of hair from my dog, Lucy.

I will put in the box...
The Holy Spirit that makes me have a new life,
The red, boiling sun that reminds me of
summertime,
A baby's first word.

I will put in the box...
My snowman that is bitter and flexible,
A tear of joy from when I was baptised,
My red bumping heart.

Alfie John Parsons (7)

The Strange Bear

Eating lunch with the bear -
Everyone says he's strange but I don't care.
He's got purple, furry ears and a thin, blue mouth.
He always wears his orange tracksuit backwards
And he lives on a colourful, bright rainbow.

He's always getting into trouble
Just as often as I'm getting stuck in a bubble.
He loves to pop candy in his mouth
And when it bangs louder than thunder in his
mouth,
It always makes me giggle.

Ini Rowaiye

Da Imaginative Oxford Scholar

My teacher told me to use my imagination,
So I wrote a poem about constipation.
Due to this, I got a crumpled, old dollar,
And then became an Oxford scholar.
I created a company and hired Timmy Failure,
And after a while, I said, "I'm gonna bail ya."
After this, I hired a big, fat creature,
Providing snacks was its best feature.
In a couple of years' time I know I will retire,
I hope I set an example for someone to admire!

William He (11)

My Dog Is Called Jax

My dog is lovely,
My dog is sweet,
He hides under the table,
Waiting for something to eat!

My dog is called Jax,
He bites Dad's socks,
His fur is dark orange,
And he looks like a fox!

Jax is a Shiba-Inu,
He is from Japan,
The way that he acts,
You would think he's a man!

My dog smells,
My dog reeks,
Instead of barking,
He loudly shrieks!

My dog is lovely,
My dog is sweet,

He nibbles my toes,
Because he thinks they're a treat!

Logan Carter (10)

Break Time!

Break time! Oh break time!
We love you! You rule!
You keep us away from the teachers in school.
While the bells are ringing,
You're still whistling.
You give us rest,
From all the hard tests in school.

Break time! Oh break time!
You are the first on my list.
We'd be in despair if you didn't exist.
We're joyful and happy,
You're awesome and cool.
Break time! Oh break time!
We love to have you!

Harry Egbayelo (10)

First Day

I walked into my new school
And immediately tried to look cool.
The main hall was frightening.
I shook like I was shocked by lightning.
I met my fellow classmates.
I needed to find some mates.
We had a tour of the school.
The lunch made me drool.
As the day came to an end
I knew my journey would take twists and bends.
I walked out of the school gates
And tomorrow I can't be late.

Joel Choe Davies (12)

Uranus

U nder the night sky, I zoomed to Uranus with my tiny dogs,

R eaching the planet, I slowly slipped on my helmet,

A nd dramatically stepped out of my house, which had turned into a rocket,

N ow I'm looking for life, but it's all dull, gloomy and turquoise,

U nder Uranus I feel as light as a feather,

S lowly I'm floating away...

Ethan Darren Walker (9)

A Day Without Humans

A world without humans
Waking up to see:
A cup of tea,
Ants on Mars, driving cars,
Rabbits becoming violent,
Tigers going silent,
Dragons painting nails,
Ghosts growing tails,
Pigeons playing chess,
Turtles making a mess,
Pigs beginning to fly,
And jaguars starting to cry...

Here I am,
In a pram,
In a world,
That is twirled,
I am the only one normal,
Which is not common!

Chejen Satchithananthan

Wonderland

The Queen of Hearts,
Loves to eat apple tarts,
She has servants shaped like cards,
Off with the heads, guards.

Her favourite colour is red,
She also has a heart-shaped bed,
She really loves to open presents,
Her room is full of cents.

She has one daughter called Lizzy,
Her hair is really frizzy,
She's the princess of Wonderland,
The queen asked for the music band.

Haseena Sophia Hamdard

A New Invention

A new invention
Is what I mentioned
Something grand
In a foreign land
Like a robot
Made of a tin pot

The colour red
Is what I said
But you made it blue
So it isn't brand new
I wanted it to do my gardening
But you made it do my mail delivering

But do not worry, it is still a new invention.

Zacharia Shafique (8)

The Stunning Snowfall

The glamorous snowflakes elegantly parachuted.
And at the bottom, it all recruited.
The children ran and squealed
As a fuzzy, white blanket steadily formed.
The surrounding environment astonishingly
transformed.
Swiftly, ravishing angels were scattered.
But briskly, the tranquil district was created
Into intimidating battles with white spheres
shattered.

Sabaa Jauhar (11)

It's Spring Time!

Spring is a time of love and care,
When everything flies through the air
Whilst caterpillars turn into butterflies,
Spiders are busy catching flies
Beetles, bugs and flies all crawl, climb and fly
Trees will blossom, with a little optimism,
As rabbits hop with a huge pop!
So spring is the time of joy and fun,
Even when it's done.

Ivani Patel (8)

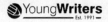

I'm Spying

I'm spying on them
This is hilarious
They can't see me
Nearly get caught
Spying

I'm spying on her
She is hiding
From her big sister
She hasn't seen me
Spying

I'm spying on them
Her mum and dad
They're filming her sister
Out in the woods
Spying

I'm spying on him
He's packing away
All the equipment
For another day
Bye.

Joe Roy (11)

Six Thousand Years Ago

Six thousand years ago
I was sleeping in bed
Then I woke up
I saw my beard
My parents had gone to school
I danced along the road, road, road
I was an adult
I was walking to work
And I was there at last
Then I went home
My parents were playing
And I told them to do homework
And they went to bed.
I was still doing my work
I was an adult.

Ovin Indiv Wasala Mudiyanselage (6)

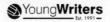

The Pie And His Friends

Once there was a pie,
who wore a very long tie,
with his friend called Cai,
and a dog called Mai,
who had one eye,
and loved to dye.

The pie had a friend called Mat,
who was a large cat,
who had a top hat,
and a pet vampire bat,
called Smelly Pat,
who loved to chat,
and that was that.

Oscar Mackenzie Terrell (9)

Non Stop Rainbow

Rainbow is colourful, Rainbow is bright.
They seem to be disappearing in the night.
When Sun and Rain kiss each other,
Seven colours emerge like a river.
Violet, indigo, followed by blue,
Green, yellow, orange and red is too.
At the end of the rainbow if you find treasure,
It gives you colourful pleasure.

Delisha Meghal Vora (7)

Friend And Foe

On these beaches so many lie,
on the golden sand,
what a dreadful dole, so many die,
and here crosses stand.

The few left alive,
barely could survive,
on the golden sand
where crosses stand.

In the trench,
what a stench!
Laughter and tears
with men's cheers.

Christmas Day,
what a play!
What a bind!
Friend and foe combined.

James Andradi

The Kitty

When I saw a kitty in space,
She was wearing a really long lace.
I took her back to my place
And I saw the kitty was witty.
When I looked at the lace,
It had a really big face,
I tried to put the kitty in space
But unfortunately, the kitty stayed in this place.
When the kitty was tired of being witty,
Everyone died in this place.

Inaya Mohamed

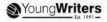

Hopeland

Hopeland is magical
Rainbow flag
Big castle
King Roo
Secret passages in the castle with hidden
doorways
Magical adventures
Light blue clouds
Rainbow sheep
Beautiful fields
Tabby cats
Silver sharks
Talking animals
Mermaids at the seashore
Magic shells
Magical powers
Hopeland is kind and helpful
Please come to Hopeland!

Hope Whittaker (5)

The Monster

I was playing Fortnite with Dion and Shae
When a monster came to take us away
I knew what to do with my computer game
I jumped inside of the TV frame
We collected the weapons and jumped out of the screen
Killing the monster, mean and clean
No monster anymore.

Rhys Thornton

Love

Love is not strong,
If you don't care,
Love is almost everywhere!

Love is our friend,
It doesn't want any war,
Love will always help out the poor!

Love will always be there,
It doesn't matter where,
Inside your heart!

Eva Maria Sirusaite (9)

If I Were A Unicorn

If I were a unicorn,
I'd fly across the sky.
Every time I would sneeze,
I would sneeze out rainbows.

My horn would be gold.
I would glide across the sunlight
With the gleaming sun.

I would be magical
And let fairies ride on me.

If only I were a unicorn.

Arabella Bage (6)

Hafsa's Rhyming Poetic World!

The swimming pool was deep, fun and blue.
In the house there was white sticky glue.
The princess girl had sparkly shoes.
Outside the museum there were long queues.
The cow was black and white and he had done a moo.
The candle was green and this is true!

Hafsa Sultan (7)

Desert

D esert is as big as a country.
E very part is dry.
S andy sand and more sand.
E very day is very hot.
R ipe cactus, green and bright.
T he desert is nice in the light.

Akshay Nar (7)

Through The Magic Door

When I went through the magic door
There was much to explore
The magic houses which could fly to the sky
Everyone knew how to fly
Characters from books just laughing around
But they weren't even standing on the ground!

Ayomide Deborah Aboyeji (10)

Cave Bear

He has a lot of black fur
His eyes look bright white in the shadows
His eyes roll, looking for meat
His teeth are white and bright
So scary, as sharp as knives.

Kai Runaghan (8)

Night Job

One night I lay in bed
Driving buses in my head.

I went into town
And I picked up a troll with a frown.

In the back things were going wrong
So I had to say... don't hit.
Don't tease the troll,
He's not that small.
Don't play with that.
Don't kick.
Don't press that.

Later on, things went well
And it got sunny.
I picked someone up.
An unusual person.
I let him on and he told me a story
And it went like this...

Something's drastic,
My nose is made of plastic.

Something's drastic,
My ears are elastic.

Something's drastic,
Something's drastic,
I'm fantastic!

Ezrianne Shaw (7)

Foxdale Primary School, Higher Foxdale

A BBQ On The Moon?

I was having a BBQ on the moon,
But when we got off the rocket,
That was when the problems started.

The raw eggs were floating
And my cat was trying to catch the cheese to have
a snack.
But while my cat was getting the cheese
She floated away instead
With cheese always just ahead!

But finally, we went home to have a peaceful night.
We went to bed.
At nine when I lay in bed
I imagined that it happened all over again.
I'll take a heavy pie next time!

Zoe Elizabeth Neuwirt (8)

Foxdale Primary School, Higher Foxdale

My Teacher Is A Dragon!

I sat at the back of the classroom
And quietly stared as my teacher started changing
And the kids all got scared.
Magically one then another horn appeared.
By lunch she was breathing fire
And smoke was coming out of her nose!
At last play she had a very long tail
Swishing by her toes.
I guess our class can be noisy,
I guess we can be loud
But our teacher turns into a dragon
And blasts a fire cloud.

Elizabeth Campbell (9)

Foxdale Primary School, Higher Foxdale

Summer Woods And Flamingo

I was walking in the summer woods,
In the beautiful flames of sunshine.
I walked past a flamingo
Who pecked me on the head!
I started to like the flamingo...
We became best friends!
Before the flamingo weed in the lake.
I laughed a lot.
He slept in the tent with me -
In the tent!
I woke early and saw him on one leg.
Saying, "Kuta-choo kuta-chew!"
My new friend, Flamingo.

Pippa Harrison (7)
Foxdale Primary School, Higher Foxdale

Food For Thought

Tell me...
How there are cod bites?
Because if cod do...
It gives me a fright!
Do sausages roll?
Do pancakes really flip?
Do carrot sticks and cucumber enjoy a nice cold dip?
Why do Rice Krispies crackle?
Why do my peas go mushy?
So many foody questions...
But I don't want to be pushy!

Lyra Kate Skillen (8)

Foxdale Primary School, Higher Foxdale

Food For Thought

Do sausages really roll?
Do fish have fingers?
Can you eat a cottage in a pie?
Where do chickens hide their chunks?
How do dogs get hot?
Do they need a fire or not?
Can potatoes wear jackets?
Do shepherds all climb in a pie
If it's cold at night?
Do cool fish really bite?

Liberty Delooze (8)
Foxdale Primary School, Higher Foxdale

My Unicorn

My unicorn, he's yellow and white
Called Onchow
He's cute but he's sneaky
He creeps out at night
Eating dynamite
He tries to blow up
My teacher when he's finished
He tells me what he's done
He has a secret den
We go there now and then.

Emily McCarrick (8)
Foxdale Primary School, Higher Foxdale

The Amazing Rugby Ball

The rugby ball was bouncing around
It hit me in the nose
I had to go to hospital
It was broken I supposed
The doctor said, "Oh dear!"
We can fix it up you know!"
He stuck two straws right up my nose
And said, "You're good to go!"

Amira Howard Murtagh (9)
Foxdale Primary School, Higher Foxdale

The Game Designer

When I grow up
I'll design games...
Crafting games
Like Minecraft
But with police
Solving crime.
A great game
A great time,
On Nintendo Switch
Xbox, PS4 and the rest.
My game will be brilliant,
It will be the best.

Ethan Thomas Hannay (7)
Foxdale Primary School, Higher Foxdale

Homework Mystery

My homework won't be in,
The wind blew it away.
My mother washed it
With my socks.
My cousin drew on it
When she came to stay.
My hamster escaped
And ripped it up.
Guess he thought
It was no good!

Connor Maginn (8)
Foxdale Primary School, Higher Foxdale

The Pirate

I saw a pirate
With a patch on his eye.
He stood on one leg
As the waves all went by.
He had a red parrot
That said 'pieces of eight'.
He had a big treasure chest
Like a big heavy weight.

Poppy Taylor-Smith (7)
Foxdale Primary School, Higher Foxdale

Surfing On A Volcano

I got my surfboard out this morning.
I thought the sea was flat and boring.
I saw a volcano
It was roaring.
I ran, jumped,
I shouted, "Heck!"
In the lava
Up to my neck,
Ouch!

Spencer Brown (8)
Foxdale Primary School, Higher Foxdale

The Monster

I whipped up my partner
I whipped up a bee
I whipped up a monster
From under the sea
The monster was scary
The monster was big
The monster was chasing
I had to be quick!

Keira Cubbon (7)
Foxdale Primary School, Higher Foxdale

Flying Around The World In A Day

One day I was given a challenge
To go around the world in a day.
I went in a flying car
And flew up, up and away!

At first, I went around to Vesuvius
Then saw it erupt with a boom!
I knew it was a burger bomb
Because it was by a café.

After that, I flew over Spain
And was greeted with "Hola" again and again,
But then I went to France
And I hated how they ate the frogs' legs.

I decided to go to space
Where the ship I made of cheese
Would definitely please the rats that went with me.

We kept on flying until
We reached the dinosaur disco on the moon!

The rats weren't happy though
Because they wanted a birthday balloon.

Next, I went to Antarctica
Which was as hot as hot,
If you boiled water
The lid would be off in a shot!

Finally, I went to England
Where all I could see was smoke,
I couldn't believe how much pollution was there,
It could have killed a goat!

Alas, I went home,
Where the people were pleased
I did this all in a day
Although the scientists hated it
Because of the book that was made called...
'Around the World in 80 Days'!

Molly Joanne Anderson (10)

St Johns CE Middle School, Bromsgrove

Hidden Ice Cream Planet

I know you won't believe me,
But sit down, have some tea.
I'm about to tell you,
That you can have ice cream for your tea!

Never trust the scientists
Or even the biologists,
Probably at this second,
They're having a secret meeting, I reckon.

They hide a secret planet,
Made of all your favourite treats,
Ice cream is the favourite
So ice cream it is, not meat!

Slurp it, hurt it, burp it,
They hide an ice cream planet!
And they won't tell a soul,
Not even if I give them ice cream in a bowl!

"Why don't they tell anyone?" I hear you say
I can't tell you that, not today.

"Please, oh please!"
Fine, whatever you say.
I thought it might be obvious
No one will believe them of course!
They'll say, "Ice Cream Planet? What rubbish!"

I mean, who would've thought?
Millions of rainbow sprinkles,
Cover the ice cream riddle,
"But why is it a riddle?"

It's all from Harry Potter,
Using the invisibility cloak,
They super-sized it,
And when they awoke
They put it over the ice cream planet!

Katie Lloyd (9)
St Johns CE Middle School, Bromsgrove

The Unusual Rocket Trip!

Now, this poem you're about to hear
Is going to burst your ear.
At least I really think it, so
Hop on board and let's go!

You're on a rocket ship,
A yellow rocket, so,
Don't press the red button,
My dearest Miss Sutton,
Hop on board and let's go!

Oh my goodness, stop your tracks,
And wake up from all your naps.
Look, there's some speakers and a moon,
We must get closer, closer soon!

Hello, Miss Sutton,
You might be surprised,
But please, oh please,
Just look to the skies!

What do you see?
You see, you see,

A scientist teaching
All about the Earth.

She is saying,
All about,
How you can't have a concert in space!

She cries, oh how she cries,
"There's only 0.1% gravity,
Go to Earth, oh Earth, oh Earth,
To have your concert, Magic Mike!"

Boom! Bang! Bash!

I wonder what's happening to the Milky Way?
Please don't answer if you're miles away!

The Earth is exploding wildly!

Leah Thompson (10)
St Johns CE Middle School, Bromsgrove

Gordon, The Heroic Guinea Pig

Gordon is my guinea pig,
He's tiny, the opposite of big.
He is everyone's hero,
His best friend is a newt called Nero.

The wind is making his cape flap
He's so high he should say goodbye to his cap.
Everybody totally adores him,
When he's around nothing is dim.

He's very fluffy, furry and cute,
He wears a coat, no way a suit.
We all know he'll save the day,
If I'm in trouble he'll be on his way.

He's not on his own, he's in a club,
They're always there, no need for a sub.
They're called the Super Squad,
There's four of them so I guess they're a quad.

I love my guinea pig,
Even though he's not big.
He's the best
Because he's so different from the rest!

Fjola O'Donnell (10)

St Johns CE Middle School, Bromsgrove

Winter Wonderland

The snow drops as light as a feather,
Leaving a soft, deep blanket covering the floor,
All trees bow down from the weight of the snow,
The glistening snowmen standing proudly.

Trees like ice sculptures cloaked in the whiteness
of snow,
As you touch the ice you feel a cold shiver up your
spine,
Delicate snowflakes gently fall,
The snow whispers all around you.

Icicles shining like crystals,
You hear the soft crunch under your feet as you
take an icy step,
On the windows the frost glistens like diamonds,
Inside by the blazing fire and with the sweetness of
hot chocolate,
Your heart is joyful on that cold, icy night,
As you look out of the window you see a winter
wonderland.

Ella Hinson (10)
St Johns CE Middle School, Bromsgrove

Chocolate Mansion

C hocolate is so yummy

H eavy, fuller, yum, yum, yum

O ver to the grass for some chocolate

C hocolate, yum, yum, yummy

O h a chocolate quilt, lovely

L ater, hot chocolate

A te chocolate, so full now

T eeth will be rotten but I don't care

E yes staring at chocolate

M arshmallow pillows, yum, yum

A nswer: Tea is always chocolate

N ice chocolate every morning

S itting on a chocolate sofa

I t never stops, yeah

O ver in the pool is chocolate

N ever stop, yes! Lots of chocolate for me!

Felicity Crowther (9)
St Johns CE Middle School, Bromsgrove

Winter

As I sit by the fire
Snowflakes are making a carpet all around.
Trees are bowing down to me,
Like they are waving.

Wear a woolly jumper
And wrap up in a silky blanket,
Keeping me warm.

Time for me to go out,
I put on my gloves, hat, scarf, boots
And very warm coat and earmuffs.

It's now bedtime.
I'm worried with all the snow
The breeze will make the tree fall down.

When it snows it's nice.
Wear extra hoodies and jumpers
So I won't freeze again.

Charlotte Collier (10)
St Johns CE Middle School, Bromsgrove

The Crazy Dino Disco

Today I went to a disco
But not any type of disco
First of all, I was in space
Not the place you'd think for a base
Second of all, there were dinosaurs
And boy they gave some mighty roars
There was even some jelly
And that went right down their belly
But the aliens came
And we didn't stop to ask their name
We were off in a flash
We even left all the mash
And then it was back home
And I planted a brand new gnome
One to add to my collection
All for my satisfaction.

Floyd Coppack Stevens (10)
St Johns CE Middle School, Bromsgrove

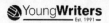

The Ruby-Red Stone

I put a stone under a hydraulic press,
My whole stomach started to fill with dread.
Eventually the stone smashed with a crash,
It looked like a very red mash.
In the stone there was a very big stash,
Of life, gold and all things bold!
At least I would never have to give it to you know
who!

Eventually he found me,
I just stood around in shock,
I can admit it, I looked like a dot.
I started to stutter and run around,
Eventually I got a stitch,
Then I ran onto a football pitch!

Ellie Booth (10)
St Johns CE Middle School, Bromsgrove

The Pidraowlacorn

The pidraowlacorn is sinister.
The pidraowlacorn is a devil from Hell.
The pidraowlacorn soars through the
pidraowlacorn eclipse.
The pidraowlacorn is chubby and cute
But on the inside he is dangerous, cruel
And a bone demolisher!
The pidraowlacorn has a sharp horn,
Sharp enough to make you sleep forever and ever.
The pidraowlacorn's hoot can kill you in seconds!
If you come across this life crusher,
It will be too late for you!

Ollie Squire (10)
St Johns CE Middle School, Bromsgrove

Snow

Snow is as soft as a blanket.
Lots of people are building snowmen.
Snow is crunchy every step you take.
We see only whiteness.

Snow is as white as paper.
People are sledging as fast as a car.
Snowflakes falling.
Slowly winter begins.
People are smelling mince pies.

The trees are bowing down
Because of all the snow.
The whiteness is blinding me in the pale sky.
The snow is as pale as a face.

Pheobie Taylor (9)
St Johns CE Middle School, Bromsgrove

Winter Is Here

I sat on my chair, by the warm, cosy fire.
I looked out the window, snow was softly swirling.
It felt like the snow was calling,
As I opened the door the snow was softly singing.

The silent water slithered like a snake down the
stream.
Soldiers of snow like an army at its edge.
The trees waving, their arms of snow dropping.
Winter's come to say hello to the winter snow.

Alivia Harriet Faulkner (9)
St Johns CE Middle School, Bromsgrove

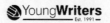
My Candy, Fluffy Floss Poem

I swam in a pool of candy
I met someone called Mandy
I went to the shops to get some meats
Instead I got lots of treats
The sweets were strawberry laces
That were stuck to our faces

Marshmallows are fluffy
But some are quite puffy
Yum yum gooey gum
You should try it, yummy, scrummy
Candyfloss... of course
We love candyfloss
And a round of applause.

Drew Dalton (9)
St Johns CE Middle School, Bromsgrove

Twenty Hyper Cats

Twenty hyper cats,
All sat on my back.
I told them to jump off my back
And go turn on the radio.
I went to go make some cakes,
I let my cousin take one
But suddenly the news turned on.
I went to see what was wrong
Then the cats played dead all day long.
The next day I went downstairs,
All the cats gave me nightmares,
All the cats were doing the hokey cokey.

Erin Elizabeth Hughes (10)

St Johns CE Middle School, Bromsgrove

Winter Wonderland

The glistening moon shines brightly through the
trees,
They sway gracefully in the cold winter breeze,
The stars are like diamonds that reflect on the
snow,
I look out of the window and see such a glow.

Our noses twitch with the cold winter breeze,
Our fingers and toes are about to freeze,
We wrap up warm to protect our skin
Because the winter days are about to begin.

Freya Snead (10)
St Johns CE Middle School, Bromsgrove

I've Got A Pet

I've got a pet
His name is Hamlet
He is a cookie monster
He can manage to fit under a stair
Like there is nothing there
He can climb up walls with his chocolate grip
But sometimes he rips the paint off the bricks.

People normally scream when they see him
But he does go to the gym
He likes chicken nuggets
And he has a friend called Toby Jugets.

Sam Dufficey (9)
St Johns CE Middle School, Bromsgrove

Shiver, Shiver

The snow seems to drop from Heaven,
Sparkling snow falling to the ground.
A thin blanket of white.
Icicles hanging from the cosy cabin.
Snowflakes dropping from the stars.
The grass has a snowy coat on.

Massive trees with snow-covered arms,
Swaying gently in the mystical wind.
The snowflakes land gently in my hair
Making me shiver to my toes.

Jack Wykes (9)
St Johns CE Middle School, Bromsgrove

Winter Wonderland

I sat by the blazing fire that crawled up the
chimney
I peeked out the window and all I could see
Was a yielding layer of snow staring at me
While I ate my dinner I saw a tree waving at me

I went outside and all I could see
Two young foxes under a tree
Hastily the snow swirled past me
The more into the night it went
The more the wind bellowed.

Isla Masson (9)
St Johns CE Middle School, Bromsgrove

Winter Wonders

Happy Advent for all around,
Eating Christmas pudding, round and round!
The cosy cabin in the middle of the snow,
I start to get scared when the blizzard starts to grow.

The iced-over lake begins to crack,
A snowy tree trips over so I have to step back.
And next to me, on the white, snowy floor,
Is an enormous Arctic fox so I run to the door.

Harrison Biddlestone (10)
St Johns CE Middle School, Bromsgrove

The Depths

Glistening in the sun as golden as a ring.
A blue sapphire surface, as smooth as a piece of glass.
Dark green weeds sway in the icy depths.
The turquoise waves splash against the coast.

Crystal-blue oceans dance in the sun.
Ships are tossed on stormy days.
The silent tide creeps up the silent sun.
The waves lap gently at the great big rocks.

Edward Melarkey (10)
St Johns CE Middle School, Bromsgrove

Winter Poem

Trees waving at winter for it has come.
Snowy mountains shining in the background.
No leaves to be seen.
Forests with sun trying to peep out
But it's too cold and too weak.

Cold animals rushing through the snow.
Snow spiralling down as fast as a bullet.
Dead gardens, too blank and white.
Cold robins perching on the bald tree.

Tom Webber (9)
St Johns CE Middle School, Bromsgrove

Winter Is Here

Winter is here,
My hands are as cold as a fridge,
The glistening moon is shining on me,
I feel cold,
There is ice on me.
I go to bed and I throw the quilt on top of me.

I can feel warmth on my numb toes
As I walk into my house,
Drinking hot chocolate, my fingers get warm,
I love it in the snow,
It is quite cold though.

William Millership (10)
St Johns CE Middle School, Bromsgrove

A Little Monster In My Room

I woke from my long sleep
And my heart started to weep
So I went downstairs.
After my horrid nightmares
I grabbed some tea
Especially made for me
And hopped back to my room
Where I had a hell of a shock.
My door was locked
I found my key, unlocked my door.
The shock I had was
That there was a little monster in my room!

Flynn Cleaver (9)
St Johns CE Middle School, Bromsgrove

My Nugget Poem

My name is Saucy Nugget,
I live in a bucket.
My friend's called Matt
But I've got more than that.
I have a big army
That loves salami.
Some are a bit psycho
But it's alright though.
Well, I mean, they do hug trees.
Wait, oh no, no, bees!
Right, got to go,
I know, what a show...
Argh! *Splat!*

Jake Shiels (10)
St Johns CE Middle School, Bromsgrove

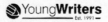
Real Life Minecraft

I had an apple
That fell from a tree
I tasted it and gobbled it
It was really tasty.

I went to the Nether
I saw a ghost
I went to the end
It made me shake
I fought the Ender Dragon
That made the ground quake.

I made a house
Out of diamond and gold
It was really bright
And really bold.

Elizabeth Green (10)
St Johns CE Middle School, Bromsgrove

Magical World

In this magical world you can see
A green, smelly pig that will scare you out of your
wits.
You can smell blue, gooey jelly.
You can hear mice whispering to one another.
Little children as slaves, what a fright!
The pig lives in a deep ditch.
You can come to Tomato Town any time
But stay away from the frightening creature!

Isabelle Johnson (10)
St Johns CE Middle School, Bromsgrove

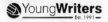

Winter's Alive

Frosty nights, frosty nights,
I like the shine of the Northern Lights.
The snow softly sings,
As I throw a snowball it gives a big bang.

All the cabin fires are all around,
I step outside and you can't hear a single sound.
While the snow falls off the trees,
The wind whips around me in a breeze.

Frederick George Spencer Parsons (9)
St Johns CE Middle School, Bromsgrove

Christmas Is Evergreen In All Our Hearts

Before the moon left the dotted sky
I wanted to say my last goodbye.
As I heard wolves howl and the birds tweet
A lonely snowflake evaporated at my feet.

I lay on the white carpet
And felt a clump of ice drip down my spine.
I never thought I would want this
To last forever and all be mine.

Josh De Waal (9)
St Johns CE Middle School, Bromsgrove

My Winter Wonderland!

Winter's breeze filling the sky
Making you shiver all night round
The fire crackling by your side
While staring at the blanket of snow.

Birds tweeting in the midnight sky
Then whispering to all their friends
The snow lying on the floor dead
Still not a movement in the forest.

Ayvah Lawther (9)
St Johns CE Middle School, Bromsgrove

Snowman In The Snow

I sat at my window with a mince pie
And heard the wolves howling outside
The shining stars up in the sky
I sat by my fire, all warm and snug.

I stepped outside and heard the birds tweeting
I walked over the icy stream
And built a snowman
And it stood there all happy and proud.

Arthur Ingram (9)
St Johns CE Middle School, Bromsgrove

Snowflakes

I was sitting by the window
Watching snowflakes fall
Holding a hot chocolate
Trying not to make it fall.

The view out the window was bright and white
And the long, pointy icicles gave me a fright
I saw the trees bow down to me
Waiting for the snow to slowly fall.

Max English (9)
St Johns CE Middle School, Bromsgrove

Winter

Winter is a cold time of year
Snow is falling all around us
Birds are tweeting too
There's a large cabin in the middle of nowhere
A fire is burning
I can smell a chicken cooking
Snow is crunchy and the ice is slippy
A forest in front of me
Trees are creaking.

Sam Wheatcroft (10)
St Johns CE Middle School, Bromsgrove

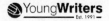

My Winter Poem

As I'm by the fire
The comfy cabin is warm
Having my hot chocolate
My hands are so warm

Stepping outside in the chilly, cold air
The snow crunches under my feet
My hands tingle as the cold air hits them
Winter has arrived
My favourite season.

Grace Rutherford (9)
St Johns CE Middle School, Bromsgrove

Winter

Icy and cold
Winter is as cold as Antarctica
The ground is white as paper
Wear your woolly jumper, it is winter.

I see nothing but whiteness
Blinding me in the dazzling sun
The trees are moving from the weight of the snow
They bow low to the floor.

Heidi Dews (9)
St Johns CE Middle School, Bromsgrove

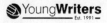

An Alien Disco

An alien disco,
As crazy as can be!
You won't be able to stop it,
It goes on until past midnight
And past 1pm.
The aliens are as crazy as can be.
Some pass out, some fall asleep
So on Mars it's as crazy as can be!

Corey Bacciochi (9)
St Johns CE Middle School, Bromsgrove

Winter Is Here

Winter is here
A chill in the air
Walking down the road
Freezing my hair.

Snow crunching under my feet
Drinking hot chocolate
In the misty forest
A blanket of snow over the road.

Harry Astin (10)
St Johns CE Middle School, Bromsgrove

![YoungWriters Est. 1991]

YOUNG WRITERS
INFORMATION

We hope you have enjoyed reading this book – and that you will continue to in the coming years.

If you're a young writer who enjoys reading and creative writing, or the parent of an enthusiastic poet or story writer, do visit our website **www.youngwriters.co.uk**. Here you will find free competitions, workshops and games, as well as recommended reads, a poetry glossary and our blog. There's lots to keep budding writers motivated to write!

If you would like to order further copies of this book, or any of our other titles, then please give us a call or visit **www.youngwriters.co.uk**.

Young Writers
Remus House
Coltsfoot Drive
Peterborough
PE2 9BF
(01733) 890066
info@youngwriters.co.uk

Join in the conversation!
Tips, news, giveaways and much more!

 YoungWritersUK   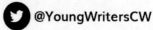 @YoungWritersCW